First published in Great Britain in 1999 by
Macdonald Young Books,
an imprint of Wayland Publishers Ltd
61 Western Road
Hove
East Sussex
BN3 1JD

You can find Macdonald Young Books on the internet at:
http://www.myb.co.uk

Text © Sam Godwin 1999
Illustrations © Caroline Jayne Church 1999
Volume © Macdonald Young Books 1999
Beginner Bees artwork © Caroline Jayne Church 1999

Commissioning editor: Dereen Taylor
Editor: Rosie Nixon
Designer: Anne Matthews
Consultant: Ann Henderson, Pre-school Learning Alliance

Printed in Hong Kong by Wing King Tong

ISBN 07500 2841 6

Charlie's
Colours

by Sam Godwin

MACDONALD YOUNG BOOKS

Charlie is a puppy, a snowy **white** puppy with a bright **blue** collar.

Look, Charlie is playing in the mud.

Whoops! Now he is white and **brown**.

Look, Charlie is playing in the field.

Whoops! Now he is white and brown and **green**.

Look, Charlie is playing in the tomato patch.

Whoops! Now he is white and brown and green and **red**.

Look, Charlie is playing among the flowers.

Whoops! Now he is white and brown and green and red and **yellow**.

Look, Charlie is playing near the tractor.

Whoops! Now he is white and brown and green and red and yellow and **black**.

Naughty puppy!

Naughty Charlie.

Whoops!

Look, Charlie is snowy **white** again.

Naughty puppy!

beginner bees

Charlie's Colours
Hb ISBN: 07500 2837 8
Pb ISBN: 07500 2841 6

Buzzy Bee's 123
Hb ISBN: 07500 2835 1
Pb ISBN: 07500 2839 4

Oscar's Opposites
Hb ISBN: 07500 2836 X
Pb ISBN: 07500 2840 8

What's that Shape?
Hb ISBN: 07500 2838 6
Pb ISBN: 07500 2842 4

All these books and many more can be purchased from your local bookseller. For more information, write to:
The Sales Department, Macdonald Young Books, 61 Western Road, Hove BN3 1JD